THE FRANCIS FRITH COLLECTION

www.francisfrith.com

First published in the United Kingdom in 2013 by The Francis Frith Collection®

This edition published exclusively for Bradwell Books in 2013
For trade enquiries see: www.bradwellbooks.com or tel: 0800 834 920
ISBN 978-1-84589-742-0

British Library Cataloguing in Publication Data

Ask Me Another! Yorkshire - A Quiz
Compiled by Julia Skinner

The Francis Frith Collection
6 Oakley Business Park,
Wylye Road, Dinton,
Wiltshire SP3 5EU
Tel: +44 (0) 1722 716 376
Email: info@francisfrith.co.uk

www.francisfrith.com

Printed and bound in Malaysia
Contains material sourced from responsibly managed forests

Front Cover: **SETTLE, CASTLEBERGH WELL AND STEPS 1924** 75792p
Frontispiece: **ASKRIGG, WOMEN OUTSIDE THE POST OFFICE 1911** 63469x

The colour-tinting is for illustrative purposes only, and is not intended to be historically accurate

CONTENTS

QUESTIONS

YORKSHIRE DIALECT WORDS

1. What in Yorkshire dialect is a 'fuzzock'?

2. What in Yorkshire dialect is a 'worrawolly'

3. What are you doing in Yorkshire if you are 'addling brass'?

4. What is the meaning of the Yorkshire dialect word 'baht'?

5. What does it mean in Yorkshire if you are 'dollypawed'?

6. What is meant in various parts of Yorkshire by the words 'gennel', 'ginnel' or 'jennel'?

7. What in Yorkshire dialect is a 'moudiwarp'?

8. If you are wearing 'keks', what are you wearing?

9. What sort of weather is 'dowly' weather?

10. What does it mean to 'fettle' something?

11. What does the Yorkshire dialect word 'saig' refer to?

12. What does 'throng' mean?

13. What does the word 'Loiner' refer to in Yorkshire?

DONCASTER, STATION ROAD 1903 49854

SPORT AND RECREATION

14. What is the name of the famous horserace which is run at Doncaster racecourse and is the oldest Classic race in Britain?

15. The oldest horseracing flat race in England is held in East Yorkshire every year. Where does it take place, and what is unusual about it?

16. Why is the horseracing course at Ripon notable in racing history?

17. What place in footballing history is held by Gillian Coultard of Yorkshire?

18. Sheffield is the home of the world's two oldest football clubs. Which are they?

19. Yorkshire is notable in footballing history for fielding the two youngest players ever to have played League football. Which clubs are they, and who were the two players?

20. What are the two links between Bradford City AFC and the popular series of Harry Potter books by J K Rowland?

21. The home of Yorkshire County Cricket Club is at the Headingley Carnegie Stadium at Leeds. County matches transferred to the ground in 1891 from the previous county pitch at Sheffield. Rugby has also been played there since 1895 by Leeds RLFC (now Leeds Rhinos), one of the 20 original clubs that formed the Rugby League. What is unique about the stadium at Headingley?

22. Rugby League was founded at a meeting in which Yorkshire town in 1895, and why?

23. Hull FC (Rugby League) holds two records in the game – what are they?

24. Why is the name of Huddersfield's Anita Lonsbrough famous in sporting history?

25. Since its formation as a 'super club' in 1963, City of Leeds Swimming Club has enjoyed great success in producing international medal winners, including an Olympic gold medal winner in the 1988 Summer Olympics at Seoul – who was he?

26. Following the 2012 Summer Olympics and Paralympics in London, the achievement of each gold-medallist in Team GB was commemorated with a pillar box being painted gold, usually in their home town. Which Olympic champions are commemorated with a gold pillar box in these six places in Yorkshire, and for which events: Horsforth, Sheffield, Leeds, Hull, Huddersfield, Skipton?

27. Filey on the North Yorkshire coast is the finishing point for The Great Yorkshire Bike Ride every June, a seventy-mile ride for charity which starts – where?

28. What is the connection between the famous Lord's Cricket Ground in London, home of the MCC, and Yorkshire?

29. What sport is played by the Sheffield Steelers?

30. Ravenscar on the North Yorkshire coast is the finishing point of which long-distance walk across the North York Moors?

ARTS AND LITERATURE

31. Haworth, a small town set amidst the moors near Keighley, is a place of literary pilgrimage, for in the parsonage there lived the Brontë sisters, Emily, Charlotte and Anne, and their brother Branwell – their father was the vicar of the Church of St Michael and All Angels. Haworth is now a place of literary pilgrimage, where The Parsonage Museum provides an insight into the sisters' lives and work. Can you name the most famous book written by each sister?

32. Which of the three famous literary Brontë sisters of Yorkshire is associated with Scarborough?

SCARBOROUGH, SOUTH BAY c1873 6560

WHITBY, THE UPPER HARBOUR c1955 W81040

33. Which famous artist was commissioned to paint Huddersfield in 1965?

34. Which North Yorkshire town is disguised as 'Darrowby' in a famous series of popular books?

35. What is the link between Whitby and Dracula, the main character in the book of that name by Bram Stoker?

FOLKLORE AND CUSTOMS

36. What in Yorkshire folklore were known as 'Gabble Retchets'?

37. What and where in Yorkshire are the Devil's Arrows?

38. Great Driffield – usually known as just Driffield – is 'the capital of the Wolds' of Yorkshire. There are several local customs linked with the new year: on New Year's Eve people gather in the market place to hear the church bells ringing in the new year, and in the first few days of the new year local children take part in 'scrambling' – what does this custom involve?

39. In the churchyard of the pretty village of Ripley, north of Harrogate, is what is claimed to be the only 'weeping cross' in Yorkshire – what was this used for?

40. Why does a Hornblower blow a horn from the corners of Ripon's market place every evening at 9pm, a custom which has taken place since the Middle Ages?

41. Why might you need earplugs on Christmas Eve if you live in Dewsbury?

42. The village of West Witton in Wensleydale is famous for which annual event?

RIPON, THE HORNBLOWER c1955 R38031

HISTORY AND ARCHAEOLOGY

43. In 1980 an ancient weapon was found on the headland on which Scarborough Castle stands, which is displayed in the visitor centre there. What is it, and why is it particularly interesting?

44. In Roman times the city of York was the principal military base in Britain, and in AD306 a general stationed there was proclaimed Emperor of Rome at York by his troops. Who was he, and why was this event significant?

45. In the 9th century York came under Viking rule. What was the Viking name for the city, and who was the last Viking king of York?

46. In former times, Yorkshire was divided into administrative areas known as the 'Ridings'. What was the origin of the Ridings, and what does the word mean?

47. When was the battle of Wakefield fought, and in which conflict?

48. Since medieval times, the title of Duke of York has traditionally been given to the second son of the sovereign. How many Dukes of York have been crowned king?

49. From medieval times until the early 20th century, the Shambles area of York was where the local butchers worked. 'Shambles' comes from 'shamels', an old word for the benches or wide shelves on which the butchers prepared and displayed meat. A 16th-century woman who lived in the Shambles area of York has been canonised as a saint – who was she?

50. How did events in Whitby in ancient times give us the expression 'a moveable feast'?

51. Why were men asked to 'Remember Scarborough' during the First World War?

52. Why can local historians in Hull claim that the first action of the Civil War of the 17th century took place in their city?

53. On the corner of Boulevard and Hessel Road in Hull stands the Fishermen's Memorial – what tragic event does this commemorate?

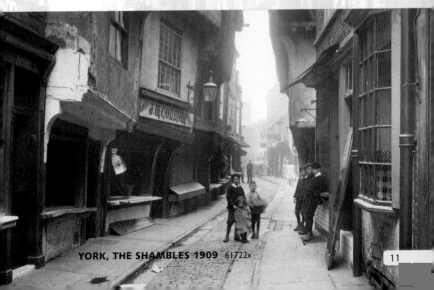

YORK, THE SHAMBLES 1909 61722x

TRADE AND INDUSTRY

54. Forster Square in Bradford was named after the Bradford Member
    of Parliament W E Forster, 'The Education King', who sponsored
    the Elementary Education Act of 1870 which provided free State
    education to children aged between 5 and 12. On the right of this
    photograph is a statue of Richard Oastler in its original position in
    Forster Square; it now stands on North Parade. He was known as
    'the Factory King' – why was this?

55. What are 'shoddy' and 'mungo', the production of which were
    important to the local economies of several Yorkshire towns in
    the past?

BRADFORD, FORSTER SQUARE 1897 39506

56. Which famous chain of High Street shops started on a market stall in Leeds in 1884?

57. In the 19th century Whitby was famous for jewellery and other items which local craftsmen made from jet – but what is jet?

58. The Cartwright Memorial Hall in Bradford was designed to hold the city's art treasures and was named in memory of Dr Edmund Cartwright, who invented the power loom that brought great wealth to Bradford in the 19th century through its important textile industry. The foundation stone for the Wool Exchange in Bradford was laid in 1864, and this proud trade house in the Venetian Gothic style was home to 3,000 dealers, with buyers and sellers trading wool from West Yorkshire, the Colonies and the Far East. It was said that whatever the type of wool or hair, a buyer would be found at the Bradford Exchange. However, in the 19th century all workers who handled wool, animal hair and hides risked catching a deadly disease, and these products were such an important part of Bradford's trade and industry, and the disease was so prevalent amongst its workers, that at one time it was known as the 'Bradford Disease' – what was it?

59. The mining of which metal was formerly a very important industry of the Yorkshire Dales?

HALIFAX, THE TOWN HALL 1900 H9001

60. Why did Halifax get the name of 'Toffee Town' in the past?

61. The tower of Sheffield's magnificent Town Hall is topped off with a bronze statue by Mario Raggi of Vulcan, who has been associated with the city for many years and appears as a supporter on its coat of arms – but who was Vulcan?

62. What was meant by the term 'rattening', which was used in Sheffield in the 19th century?

63. What in the past were known as 'Tom Puddings', which were particularly associated with the port at Goole?

64. The town of Pontefract is famous for its Pontefract Cakes (or 'Pomfret' or 'Pomfrey' Cakes). What are these made of?

SHEFFIELD, THE TOWN HALL 1896 37422

General Knowledge – Yorkshire

65. During the reign of King John (1199-1216) the castle at Knaresborough served as a royal arsenal for the manufacture of 'quarrels' – what were these?

66. Which notorious highwayman was arrested in East Yorkshire, tried in York Assizes and held in the condemned cell of York Prison before his execution in 1739?

67. What were known as 'blind backs' in Leeds in the past?

68. Where in York can you find a depiction of a monkey's funeral?

69. What are Yorkshire Fat Rascals?

70. Egton Bridge on the North York Moors near Whitby is famous for its annual show for which fruit?

**KNARESBOROUGH
THE CASTLE 1892**
30611

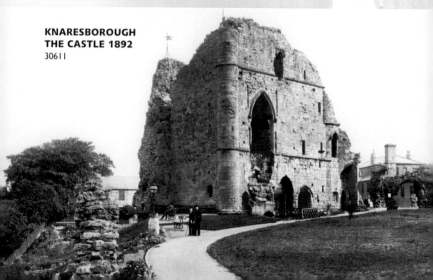

HARROGATE, THE ROYAL PUMP ROOM 1902 48974

71. Harrogate claims to have the world's strongest known sulphur springs – how does the water in Harrogate's springs get its mineral content?

72. The inventor of the flushing toilet was a South Yorkshire man. Who was he, and where was he born?

73. Which South Yorkshire company invented an essential household item used in kitchens and bathrooms?

74. An old Yorkshire saying of the past was: 'From Hull, Hell and Halifax, good Lord deliver us.' What was the origin of this saying?

75. Rotherham Minster is famous for an unusually large number of … what?

76. What is the link between Harrogate and the theme tune of the long-running BBC radio serial 'The Archers'?

77. Semerwater is the second largest natural lake in North Yorkshire after Malham Tarn, about half a mile in length and covering about 100 acres. It was formed by Ice Age glaciers forming in the side dale known as Raydale, and is drained by England's shortest river – which river is this?

78. What is peculier (yes, that is the correct spelling!) about the Wensleydale town of Masham?

79. One of 'the wonders of the waterways system' can be found on the Leeds & Liverpool Canal near Bingley – what is it?

SEMERWATER 1929 82610

80. The highest inn in England can be found in Yorkshire – where is it?

81. Bathing machines are seen lined up on the beach at Scarborough in the photograph on page 6, overlooked by the imposing Grand Hotel – what is unusual about this building?

82. Which natural feature in North Yorkshire is known as 'the Matterhorn of Cleveland'?

83. Burnby Hall Gardens at Pocklington in East Yorkshire are where you will find the United Kingdom's national collection of which plants?

84. How did 'The Flying Man of Pocklington' meet his end in 1733, and how is he still remembered in this East Yorkshire town?

85. A word found in names for a natural feature in many parts of North Yorkshire is a 'foss' – what does this mean?

86. Who holds the title of 'Admiral of the Humber'?

87. Where can you find Yorkshire's last working windmill?

88. Whereabouts in Yorkshire will you find a railway viaduct that is nicknamed 'the Virgin Viaduct'?

89. Which place in West Yorkshire is so magnificent that it has been called 'The Hampton Court of the North'?

90. Selby has one of the most magnificent parish churches in England, the former abbey church of Selby Abbey which was closed in 1539. Inside the church is a link with George Washington, the first President of the USA. What is it?

91. What is the link between a South Yorkshire village and the American custom of Thanksgiving, observed in the United States on the 4th Thursday in November each year?

92. What are the famous 'Three Peaks' of the Yorkshire Dales?

93. Which Yorkshire town has given its name to a special type of lamb chop?

94. Wensleydale Cheese is a favourite delicacy of which animated film character?

SELBY, GOWTHORPE 1918 68168

HAWES, HAYMAKING 1924 75754

95. Which item of road safety was invented and produced in Halifax?

96. Market Weighton in East Yorkshire was once famous as the home of 'the Yorkshire Giant' – who was he?

97. What is the link between Doncaster and the fastest steam locomotive in the world?

98. Bradford's City Hall is adorned at the second floor level with 35 statues of Kings and Queens of England and the United Kingdom – except for that of one person. Who is it?

99. Why might animals in the centre of Harrogate have been impounded for 'gate-crashing' in the past?

HAREWOOD HOUSE c1886 7365

100. Harewood House, between Leeds and Harrogate, is one of
Yorkshire's finest stately homes. It was designed by John
Carr and Robert Adam, and the north front of the house was
remodelled in 1843 by the great Victorian architect Sir Charles
Barry, who also designed the Houses of Parliament. The house
contains many treasures, including an unrivalled collection of
18th-century furniture made especially for Harewood by which
great furniture designer, who was born at Otley, also in West
Yorkshire?

101. The Labour politician Harold Wilson (1916-1995) was born and
educated in Huddersfield, and a statue of him stands in front of
the town's railway station. He served two terms as Britain's Prime
Minister, from 1964 to 1970, and again from 1974 to 1976. Harold
Wilson was famously fond of an item of clothing made in West
Yorkshire – what was it, and where was it made?

102. What did it mean if you became a 'Frithman' in Beverley in the past?

103. Holy Trinity Church in Richmond was unlike any other church in the country when this photograph was taken, because it had shops built into its northern walls. A number of shop buildings have since been removed from around the tower, but many still remain lower down. Part of the church is now used a museum commemorating which army regiment with local associations?

104. A song that is always associated with Yorkshire is 'On Ilkla Moor Baht'at' ('On Ilkley Moor Without a Hat').
What is the origin of this song?

105. Who was voted 'the Greatest Ever Yorkshireman' in a BBC poll in 2000?

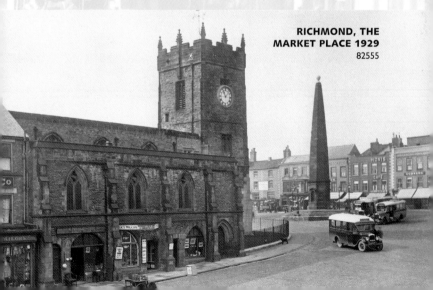

RICHMOND, THE MARKET PLACE 1929
82555

ANSWERS

YORKSHIRE
DIALECT WORDS

1. A 'fuzzock' is a donkey.

2. A 'worrawolly' is a simpleton, or a fool.

3. 'Addling brass' is a Yorkshire expression for earning money.

4. 'Baht' is a Yorkshire dialect word for 'without' – as in the title of the song 'On Ilkla Moor Baht'at' ('On Ilkley Moor Without a Hat').

5. 'Dollypawed' means left-handed.

6. 'Gennel', 'ginnel' or 'jennel' are words used in various parts of Yorkshire for a narrow alleyway between houses.

7. 'Moudiwarp' is a Yorkshire dialect word for a mole.

8. 'Keks' are trousers.

9. 'Dowly' is miserable, damp or dreary weather.

LEEDS, THE POST OFFICE AND REVENUE OFFICE 1897 39088

10. To 'fettle' something is to clean it, or to put it in good order.

11. 'Saig' is a dialect word for a saw, thus 'saigins' means sawdust.

12. 'Throng' means busy, as in 'It was throng in there!'

13. A 'Loiner' is the name for an inhabitant of Leeds, derived from the word 'Loin' for a roll of cloth, reflecting the importance of Leeds as a centre of the cloth industry in the past.

SPORT AND RECREATION

14. There have been horserace meetings in Doncaster since 1600, but it was the St Leger that was first run in 1776 that put the town on the racing calendar. The race was named after a neighbour of Lord Rockingham, Lt Gen Anthony St Leger, and is the oldest Classic race.

15. Claimed to be the oldest horseracing flat race in England, the annual Kipling Cotes Derby is held near Market Weighton in East Yorkshire each March. The race dates from 1519 and is run over a 4-mile course over farm lanes and tracks. Each rider pays an entrance fee, and the money thus raised is given to the rider who comes second, whilst the winner receives the interest on a sum of money that was invested back in 1618 – consequently, the rider who comes second often receives more prize money than the actual winner!

16. The horseracing course at Ripon is notable in racing history for staging Britain's first race for female riders, which took place in 1723.

17. A famous sports personality from Thorne near Doncaster is Gillian Coultard, who captained the England women's football team in the 1990s, and was capped over 120 times for representing her country, the first woman and amateur player to reach over 100 caps for England. She also has a place in footballing history as the first woman to have scored a goal at Wembley stadium.

18. Sheffield is the home of the world's two oldest football clubs. Sheffield FC, founded in 1857, is still in existence, playing at the Don Valley Stadium. Hallam FC, founded three years later, is also still in existence, playing at its original ground, Sandygate. Bramall Lane, home of Sheffield United FC, is thought to be the oldest major ground which still hosts professional football matches. It is also one of only two grounds to have staged an England cricket match against Australia, an England football international, and an FA Cup final (the Oval in London is the other). The name of Sheffield Wednesday FC was originally 'the Wednesday Cricket Club'. A cricket team of that name was established in the early 19th century and later a football team was set up in association with it. For many years the football club was known as 'The Wednesday', before its official name was changed to Sheffield Wednesday FC in the late 1920s.

19. For many decades Albert Geldard held the record as the youngest player ever to play League football. He was 15 years and 158 days old when he made his debut for Bradford (Park Avenue) FC in 1929. He also represented England before his 20th birthday. His record was broken in the 2008/09 season, when Reuben Noble-Lazarus came on to play for Barnsley Football Club at Ipswich Town aged 15 years and 45 days.

20. Bradford City AFC's scarves in the club's distinctive colours of claret and amber are popular with fans of the 'Harry Potter' books, as they are also the colours of Hogwarts School – and Bradford City actually had a player called Harry Potter before the First World War!

21. The Headingley stadium is unique, as it is effectively two grounds, for both cricket and rugby, unified by a stand which has one side facing the cricket pitch and one side facing the rugby pitch.

22. Rugby League was founded at a meeting at the George Hotel in Huddersfield in 1895, when twenty-two clubs met at the George Hotel and formed the NRFU (Northern Rugby Football Union) as a breakaway group from the RFU (Rugby Football Union). This revolution in the world of rugby was sparked by the RFU's decision to enforce the amateur principle of the sport. The NRFU became the Rugby Football League in 1922.

23. Hull FC's Lee Jackson holds the record for the fastest ever try in a professional game; playing against Sheffield Eagles at the Don Valley Stadium in 1992, he scored after just nine seconds. In the 1978/79 season in Division Two, Hull FC won every game – the only time this has been achieved in professional Rugby League.

24. The swimming baths that used to stand in Ramsden Street in Huddersfield were where the 1960 Olympic champion Anita Lonsbrough trained. Born in Huddersfield in 1941, she worked at the Town Hall as a clerk. At the age of 19 she won a gold medal in the 200m breaststroke event at the 1960 Olympics in Rome in a thrilling final in world record time, and received a hero's welcome on her return home to Huddersfield. At one time in her career she held not only the Olympic gold medal but also the Empire and European gold medals at the same time. She also made sporting history by becoming the first woman to win the BBC Sports Personality of the Year award in 1962, and was the first woman to carry the flag for the British team at the Olympics, at Tokyo in 1964.

25. Adrian Moorehouse, who won the gold medal in the 100m breaststroke event at the Seoul Olympics.

**WETHERBY, HIGH STREET
1909** 61730

26. Horsforth: Alistair Brownlee – Men's Triathlon. Sheffield: Jessica Ennis – Women's Heptathlon. Leeds: Nicola Adams – Boxing, Women's Flyweight. Hull: Luke Campbell – Boxing, Men's Bantamweight. Huddersfield: Ed Clancy – Cycling, Men's Team Pursuit. Skipton: Danielle Brown – Archery, Women's Individual Compound.

27. The Great Yorkshire Bike Ride starts at Wetherby Racecourse.

28. The founder of the famous Lord's Cricket Ground in London, home of the MCC, was a North Yorkshire man, Thomas Lord, who was born in Thirsk in 1755, in a house that is now the town museum.

29. Ice hockey.

30. Ravenscar is the finishing point of the 40-mile Lyke Wake Walk for which Osmotherley on the western edge of the North Yorks Moors is the usual starting point. The Lyke Wake Walk crosses the moors by their highest points and has to be completed within 24 hours. The successful walkers then become members of the Lyke Wake Club.

ARTS AND LITERATURE

31. The wild moorland landscapes around Haworth surely gave the Brontë sisters the inspiration for their novels, the most famous of which are 'Jane Eyre' (Charlotte Brontë), 'Wuthering Heights' (Emily Brontë) and 'The Tenant of Wildfell Hall' (Anne Brontë).

32. Anne Brontë, the youngest of the famous Brontë sisters, loved Scarborough and visited many times; she used the town as the background to her novel 'Agnes Grey'. She died in Scarborough in 1849, and her grave is at the northern end of St Mary's churchyard in the town.

33. L S Lowrie. His painting can be seen in Huddersfield Art Gallery.

HAWORTH, TOP WITHENS, 'WUTHERING HEIGHTS' 1958 H194045

THIRSK, MARKET DAY c1955 T306030

34. Thirsk, south of Northallerton, was disguised as 'Darrowby' in the much loved 'James Herriot' series of books about life in a country veterinary practice in the past. The actual vet in the books, whose real name was Alf Wight, lived in and practised from a surgery at 23 Kirkgate in Thirsk (now 'The World of James Herriot' visitor attraction), and married his wife Joan in St Mary's Church in the town in 1941. However, the popular BBC TV series of the 1970s and 80s based on the James Herriot books, 'All Creatures Great and Small', used the Wensleydale village of Askrigg as the location for 'Darrowby'.

35. Bram Stoker, author of the Gothic horror novel 'Dracula', stayed in Whitby in 1890, at Number 6, Royal Crescent; it was there that he started to write his famous book, setting much of it in the town. Whitby's parish church of St Mary which overlooks the harbour features in the book as the place where the count sought refuge in the grave of a suicide.

FOLKLORE AND CUSTOMS

36. An old folklore belief in the Leeds area of Yorkshire was that the souls of babies who died before they were baptised would return to haunt their parents, in the shape of devil dogs known as Gabble Retchets.

37. The Devil's Arrows are a group of three huge standing stones (originally there were four, or perhaps five), that stand close to the A1 near Boroughbridge in North Yorkshire; the site is one of the most famous prehistoric monuments in the county, probably dating from around 2000BC. The stones were brought there from Knaresborough, about six miles away. They range from 18ft to 22ft in height (taller than most of the Stonehenge megaliths) and weigh more than 20 tons each. The unusual deep and curiously fluted grooves are believed to be the result of weathering. They stand in a line running north to south and at intervals of 200ft to 370ft. In Aubrey Burl's paper on the Arrows in the 1991 Yorkshire Archaeological Journal he explains that the Devil's Arrows possess all the features of a classic stone row, in that this alignment leads uphill from water; has a blocking or terminal stone at its lower end; the stones of the row are graded in height with the tallest at the head of the gradient near a stretch of level ground; and the row has an apparent alignment on the most southerly Midsummer rising moon. One legend associated with this site says that the stones were thrown by the Devil from Howe Hill (near Fountains Abbey) to destroy Aldborough, but (as often happens to be the case) the Devil missed his target. Another story says that you can raise the Devil if you walk widdershins (anti-clockwise, or anti-sunwise) around the stones twelve times at midnight.

BOROUGHBRIDGE, THE DEVIL'S ARROWS
1895 35295

38. When children in Driffield go 'scrambling' in the New Year, they walk through the town calling out a traditional rhyme and are given sweets, money and other gifts by shopkeepers.

39. Around the base of the 'weeping cross' at Ripley are eight niches in which sinners might kneel, repent and seek forgiveness.

40. At 9pm every evening in Ripon, four blasts are sounded on a horn from each corner of the Market Place as the Hornblower 'sets the watch'. The tradition dates back to medieval times when local people paid an annual fee to maintain a series of constables who acted as nightwatchmen for the town; the constables were appointed by the 'Wakeman', who was elected each year from 12 Aldermen of the town. Anyone whose home was robbed after the sounding of the horn could claim compensation if it could be proved that the Wakeman and his constables had been negligent in their duties.

41. A custom at Dewsbury is for a bell of the parish church called 'Black Tom' to be rung on Christmas Eve, with a toll for every year of the Christian era. This means that the bell is now rung over 2,000 times; as the tolling has to finish at midnight, it currently begins just after 10pm.

42. West Witton holds an annual event called the Bartle Burning, when an effigy named Owd Bartle is carried around the village in a procession before being burnt, whilst a traditional rhyme is called out by the Chanter. It takes place on the Saturday nearest to 24th August, the Feast Day of St Bartholomew, to whom the village church is dedicated. One theory about the custom's origin is that Owd Bartle was a notorious sheep stealer in medieval times and it commemorates him being caught by local farmers and tried in the village church court.

HISTORY AND ARCHAEOLOGY

43. In 1980 a Bronze Age sword was found on the headland at Scarborough which is about 3,000 years old; it was found almost perfectly preserved, not broken, and can be seen at the visitor centre at Scarborough Castle.

44. It was at York in AD306 that Constantine the Great was proclaimed Emperor of Rome by his army – he went on to make Christianity the official religion of the Roman Empire. A modern statue of Constantine stands outside York Minster, but a marble head of him sculpted in Roman times, found in Stonegate, can be seen in the Yorkshire Museum in the city.

45. The Viking name for York was 'Jorvik'. The last Viking king of Jorvik was the delightfully-named Eric Bloodaxe, who died in AD954. Excavations in York have turned up many artefacts from its Viking period, which can be seen at The Jorvik Viking Centre.

46. It was the Viking Danes who settled in Yorkshire who first divided the county into the 'ridings', three historic subdivisions of the county (North, East and West Riding) which were abolished in 1974 under local government reorganisation. Originally, they were called 'thridings', or thirds.

47. The battle of Wakefield in 1460, at which Richard, Duke of York was killed, was one of the major battles of the Wars of the Roses.

48. Six Dukes of York have become reigning monarchs. They are: Edward IV, Henry VIII, Charles I, James II, George V and George VI.

49. A butcher's wife who lived in the Shambles at York in the 16th-century was Margaret Clitheroe. This was a time of religious persecution, and she was found guilty of harbouring Roman Catholic priests and was sentenced to death in 1586 by 'pressing', being crushed to death beneath a board. She was canonized by Pope Paul VI in 1970 as St Margaret Clitheroe, sometimes known as 'the Pearl of York', and a house in the Shambles is set aside as a shrine to her.

50. Whitby's famous abbey was founded in AD657 by a Northumbrian princess called Hilda – later to be St Hilda – who was its first abbess. In AD664 the Synod of Whitby was held at Whitby Abbey to resolve the differences between Celtic and Roman Christianity, particularly over calculating the date of Easter. Following the synod, the English Church was unified under the Roman discipline, and the date of Easter Day was settled as the first Sunday after the Paschal full moon. Because Easter itself is a holy day whose date is not fixed to a particular day of the calendar year, the dates of all the other Christian festivals – or 'feasts' – which are linked to it are also changeable, in response to the date of Easter for that year, and thus are known as 'moveable feasts'. Easter itself can also be called a 'moveable feast'.

51. On 17 August 1914, during the First World War, two German cruisers took up station off Scarborough and fired over 500 shells into the town. A number of people were killed, and this action spawned a slogan for the enlistment posters all over the country that urged young men to join up and fight the enemy. It ran: 'Remember Scarborough? Enlist Now!'

HULL, WHITEFRIARGATE 1903 49817

52. On 23rd April 1642, King Charles I was refused entry to Hull through the Beverley Gate, at the west end of Whitefriargate; this was the first action of defiance against the king of the Civil War. It was in a room now known as the 'Plotting Parlour' in Ye Olde White Harte Inn (then the Governor's home) that the Governor and other leading citizens decided to follow Parliament's instructions and refuse to let the king enter Hull and take control of the arsenal that was stored in the city.

53. The Fisherman's Memorial in Hull depicts a statue of George Smith, skipper of the Hull trawler 'Crane', who was killed during an incident known as 'The Russian Outrage' which occurred in 1904. Russia was at war with Japan, and in the early hours of 22 October 1904 the Russian fleet opened fire on a group of Hull trawlers fishing on the Dogger Bank, mistaking them for Japanese torpedo boats.

TRADE AND INDUSTRY

54. Richard Oastler was known as 'The Factory King' because he fought against the use of child labour in the industrial mills of Britain in the 18th and 19th centuries. In the early days of the Industrial Revolution, the children who worked in the mills around Leeds were luckier than those who worked at Bradford: in Leeds they only had to work a 12-hour day, against a 13-hour day in Bradford. Even children as young as five were sometimes expected to work these hours.

55. 'Shoddy' and 'mungo' were types of material made by recycling old rags and cloth clippings. Recycled rags mixed with virgin wool made 'shoddy', and 'mungo' was when tailors' clippings of cloth were mixed into the process. Major centres of the 'shoddy' industry in Yorkshire in the past were Ossett, Batley and Dewsbury, which re-used old woollen items to make heavy woollens such as blankets and military uniforms.

56. Marks & Spencer. The Lithuanian immigrant Michael Marks opened his first Penny Bazaar stall in Leeds in 1884, selling buttons, wool, socks and stockings, before moving to Skipton where he co-founded Marks and Spencer with Tom Spencer.

57. Jet is a hard, black material which is actually fossilised wood from Araucaria trees (a type of Monkey Puzzle tree). Twenty million years ago there must have been a forest of these trees around the Whitby area, which has one of the best deposits of jet anywhere in the world.

58. In the 19th century all workers who handled wool, animal hair and hides risked catching anthrax. These products were an important part of Bradford's trade and industry, and the deadly disease was so prevalent amongst its workers that anthrax at one time was known as the 'Bradford Disease'. In the 1890s Frederick William Eurich was appointed to work in a laboratory in Bradford. After years of experiments which put him in considerable danger, Eurich realised the disease was transferred to humans via blood from an infected animal. The use of formaldehyde, rigorous precautions and inspection of wool and other fibres led to a decrease in cases of anthrax, and in later years the development of antibiotics provided a cure for the disease. Eurich was awarded the Gold Medal of the Textile Institute in recognition of the thousands of lives in the textile industry that were saved as a result of his work.

59. Lead mining was an important industry in the Yorkshire Dales in the past, especially around Grassington, Gunnerside and Reeth. Another centre was Pateley Bridge, with many lead mines around Greenhow Hill.

60. Halifax became known as 'Toffee Town' because it was there that John Mackintosh invented his famous toffee in the 1890s, a cross between traditional English toffee which was rock hard and American toffee in the soft caramel style. He and his wife first sold the toffee from their pastry shop at King Cross. John Mackintosh's company merged with Rowntree of York in 1988, but his most famous creation is still popular – Quality Street.

61. Vulcan was the Roman god of fire and furnaces, and thus most appropriate for Sheffield with its history of iron and steel production. The statue on top of Sheffield's Town Hall depicts a large nude figure holding a hammer in his right hand and arrows in his left, with his right foot resting on an anvil. Sheffield is historically famous for its cutlery industry, which was first recorded in 1297, when 'Robertus le coteler' – Robert the cutler – was listed as a taxpayer. In 1624, 498 master craftsmen in Sheffield and the surrounding villages were recorded as making various items of cutlery, blades and other associated products: 440 knife makers, 31 shear and sickle makers, and 27 scissor makers. By the mid 17th century the industry was run by master craftsmen – 'little mesters' – doing business from small workshops attached to their cottages or at water-powered grinding wheels. Here might be a coal-fuelled smithy where blades were forged, or small rooms where the handles were fitted or 'hafted', and where knives were finally assembled after the blades had been taken to a riverside cutlers' wheel to be ground on a grindstone. Sheffield's once-great cutlery industry has now all but disappeared, but the creation of a new public plaza outside the city's railway station with water features and a giant steel sculpture representing a knife blade, known as 'The Cutting Edge', has ensured that Sheffield's proud industrial heritage is never forgotten.

62. 'Rattening', which originally referred to rats destroying human belongings, took on a more sinister meaning during the 'Sheffield Outrages' of the second half of the 19th century, when trade unionists were accused of threatening non-union members by means of arson, intimidation and murder. It became the term used for the confiscation of a workman's tolls on behalf of trade societies to persuade workers to join a union or to make them stop working for masters paying less than the recommended rate.

KNOTTINGLEY, FERRYBRIDGE POWER STATION c1960 K82038

63. In the past, coal was carried from Yorkshire coal mines down the Aire and Calder Navigation to the port at Goole in vessels called 'Tom Puddings', short containers that could be coupled together in any length and then towed by barges. When they reached their destination, they were lifted with a hoist and turned upside down so the coal could be emptied out – just like a pudding being turned out from a pudding bowl. A barge hauling 'Tom Puddings' loaded with coal can be seen near the Ferrybridge power station at Knottingley, West Yorkshire, in this photograph.

64. Liquorice. The Crusaders of the 12th century probably introduced the liquorice plant to Pontefract, and from that grew a hugely important industry; it still flourishes today, but the liquorice roots are no longer grown locally. The disc-shaped sweets flavoured with liquorice known as Pontefract Cakes (or 'Pomfret' or 'Pomfrey' Cakes) are still made in the town, and an annual liquorice festival is held there, where liquorice flavoured cheese, ice cream and beer can be sampled. Liquorice is known as 'Spanish' in some parts of Yorkshire.

65. 'Quarrels' were the missiles fired from crossbows – these missiles had a four-sided sharply pointed metal head, which could cause considerable damage to buildings and fearsome wounds. The phrase 'to pick a quarrel' derives from the crossbow-man choosing the best weapon to use against a particular target.

66. Dick Turpin, who regularly stayed at the Ferry Inn on Station Road in Brough-on-Humber under the alias of John Palmer. He was arrested there under that name in 1738 and sent to York Castle to be tried at the Assizes for his many crimes, including murder,  in 1739. He spent his final days in the condemned cell of York's prison, and was hanged at the gallows at Tyburn, on the Tadcaster Road. Dick Turpin's grave can be seen in St George's churchyard. Turpin is famous in folklore for a legendary ride on his famous horse, Black Bess, from London to York, but this ride was actually done 60 years earlier by another highwayman, William Nevison, who was also hanged at York, in 1684.

67. One feature of the housing built for the industrial workers of Leeds in the past was the style of houses known as 'blind-backs', which had no rear windows or doors. From the end elevation they looked like a house that had been cut in half with one half pulled down.

YORK, THE MINSTER FROM THE SOUTH WEST 1909 61705

68. In York Minster, where one panel of a medieval window depicts what is known as 'The Monkey's Funeral'. Nine monkeys are pictured. The deceased is carried shoulder-high by four pallbearers, while a bell-ringer leads the procession with a cross-bearer behind. The bereaved young monkey is in the centre foreground, being comforted by a friend. Last but not least, one monkey is sampling the wine as the funeral feast. York Minster is famous for wonderful Gothic architecture, woodwork and stonework, and especially stained glass, 128 windows in all. It is particularly famous for its magnificent Rose Window and the beautiful west window with heart-shaped tracery, known as 'the Heart of Yorkshire'. The wonderful stained glass window above the high altar was made in the 13th century and is larger than a tennis court. Re-leading of the window was begun when it was removed from the minster for safety during the Second World War; the mammoth task took ten years to complete.

69. Yorkshire Fat Rascals are delicious fruited teacakes with a rich crust which are a popular delicacy in Yorkshire tea rooms. They are a sort of cross between scones and rock cakes. Originally they would have been cooked either on a 'backstone' or on a griddle over a turf fire, and were also known as turf cakes in the past.

70. Egton Bridge is famous for its annual gooseberry show, held in August. It is the oldest gooseberry show in the country, having been established in 1800. The 2009 show saw local man Bryan Nellist take the prize for the heaviest gooseberry ever grown in the UK, a feat later recognised as a world record. His Woodpecker berry weighed 2.19oz (62.0 grams), beating the previous 16-year record set by Kelvin Archer from Cheshire.

71. The sulphurous content of the water in Harrogate's mineral springs is the result of magmatic or plutonic waters rising from deep within the earth's crust. The sulphurous water which made the place famous as a spa town was a recommended cure for the intestinal worms and other kinds of internal parasites which in the late 17th century were said to have affected much of the population. One of the strangest things about Harrogate's famous mineral wells is that, of the scores of springs which reach the surface, no two are exactly alike in the chemical analysis of their water.

72. The inventor of the flushing toilet was Thomas Crapper, who was born at Thorne near Doncaster in 1837.

73. The Rotherham brass founders Guest and Chrimes are credited with inventing the household tap – the company patented and manufactured the first screw-down tap mechanism in 1845.

74. Set in the foothills of the Pennines, Halifax is one of the great cloth towns of England and has been a producer of cloth since the 13th century. The cloth industry was so important to Halifax that in medieval times the town was granted its own laws for dealing with people convicted of stealing cloth; those found guilty were beheaded on a guillotine-like contraption called the 'Halifax Gibbet'. The Halifax Gibbet Law was limited to the forest of Hardwick and the 18 towns and villages within its boundary. Anyone found with stolen cloth 'shall be taken to the gibbet and there have his head cut from his body'. This law, combined with the harsh anti-vagrancy laws of Hull, gave rise to the saying 'From Hull, Hell and Halifax, good Lord deliver us.'

HALIFAX, THE OLD GIBBET
H9095

75. Rotherham Minster is renowned for the faces of over 30 'Green Men' which can be found hidden amidst the carved foliage that decorates the pillars of the nave. Although it probably derived from a pagan symbol, perhaps symbolising a fertility figure or a nature spirit, a carving of a Green Man is commonly found in medieval churches and is believed to have been used as a symbol of spring, or rebirth; however, it is most unusual to find as many examples of Green Men in one church as there are in Rotherham Minster.

76. The theme music of the BBC radio programme 'The Archers' was composed by Arthur Wood, deputy conductor of the Harrogate Municipal Orchestra. Mr Wood wrote the music as the 'Barwick Green' movement in his symphony entitled 'My Native Heath'.

77. England's shortest river, which drains Semerwater, is the River Bain, which runs into Wensleydale at Bainbridge.

78. Masham is the home of Theakston Brewery, famous for its potent 'Old Peculier' beer.

79. The five rise locks at Bingley are part of the Leeds & Liverpool Canal, and are one of the wonders of the waterway system. They are known as staircase locks, because the top gate of each chamber is also the bottom one of the next: there is no water between the two.

BINGLEY, FIVE RISE LOCKS, LEEDS & LIVERPOOL CANAL c1900 B98501

80. The Tan Hill Inn, occupying a desolate moorland location on Sleightholme Moor between Swaledale and the valley of the Greta to the north, is the highest inn in England. For many years it was the site of an annual sheep sale; today it is a welcome refreshment stop for walkers on the Pennine Way.

81. The Grand Hotel at Scarborough has 365 bedrooms, 52 chimneys, 12 floors and 4 turrets, representing the days, weeks, months and seasons of the year. It was the largest brick building in Europe when it opened in 1867.

82. Near Great Ayton, on the border between North Yorkshire and the borough of Redcar & Cleveland, is Roseberry Topping, a distinctive sandstone hill with a jagged edge that is known as 'the Matterhorn of Cleveland'.

83. The lakes at Burnby Hall Gardens at Pocklington are home to the United Kingdom's national collection of hardy water lilies, actually the largest such collection in Europe.

84. Pocklington was the scene of a tragic death in 1733 when the showman Thomas Pelling, 'The Flying Man', tried to fly from the tower of the town's parish church using a pair of home-made wings; he was killed when he collided with a buttress and a plaque on the church records that he was buried 'exactly under the place where he died'. The event is recalled in Pocklington's annual Flying Man Festival, a weekend themed around aerial and flying activities.

85. 'Foss' is an old Norse word for a waterfall.

86. The title of 'Admiral of the Humber' is held by the Lord Mayor of Hull.

87. Yorkshire's last working windmill is at Skidby in East Yorkshire. Built in 1821, the four-storey tower mill is preserved as part of the Museum of East Riding Rural Life.

88. At Tadcaster, near Selby. The eleven-arched railway viaduct was built in 1849, but never used – the railway that should have crossed it was never constructed, so it became known as 'The Virgin Viaduct'.

89. Temple Newsam, a grand Tudor-Jacobean house near Leeds, is often dubbed 'The Hampton Court of the North'. It is now an important museum and art gallery.

90. The 14th-century Washington Window in the parish church at Selby features the heraldic arms of the Washington family, ancestors of George Washington, the first president of the USA. The design of the Washington Coat of Arms is believed to have been the inspiration for the American flag of the Stars and Stripes.

91. Austerfield, near Doncaster, was the birthplace in 1590 of William Bradford, one of the Pilgrim Fathers who sailed for America on board the 'Mayflower' in 1620, and went on to become the Governor of Plymouth Colony in Massachusetts. William Bradford is credited as the instigator of the American Thanksgiving celebration, when in 1621 the Plymouth colonists and Wampanoag Native Americans shared an autumn harvest feast to give thanks for a successful bounty of crops.

92. The Three Peaks of Yorkshire are Ingleborough, Whernside and Pen-y-Ghent.

93. Barnsley – a Barnsley chop is cut from the centre of the loin across both chops, producing a butterfly shape, and is believed to have originated from the Brooklands Hotel in the town.

94. The delicious Wensleydale Cheese has become famous as a favourite of the Wallace character in the 'Wallace and Gromit' animated films, and the Wensleydale Creamery at Hawes produces a special brand of 'Wallace and Gromit Wensleydale'.

95. It was in Halifax in the 1930s that Percy Shaw patented 'cat's eyes', or reflecting road studs, and produced them at his company in the town. James May, a presenter on BBC TV's 'Top Gear', said of Mr Shaw's simple but effective invention that "this little block of iron and rubber has probably done more to save lives on the road than anything since".

96. Market Weighton was the home of William Bradley, believed to have been the tallest ever man in Britain. He was born in 1787, and grew to be 7 feet 9 inches tall. He travelled the country as 'the Yorkshire Giant' before retiring to Market Weighton, where he died in 1820. A plaque outside his house in York Street shows the size of the shoes he used to wear, and he is remembered in his home town with an event known as 'Giant Bradley Day' each year. The extra-large chair that he used can still be seen in the Londesbrough Arms in the town.

97. Doncaster became an important industrial centre in the 19th century, after the Great Northern Railway chose it for the site of its locomotive and carriage and wagon workshops. The Doncaster Plant was particularly famous for building LNER 2, 4, and 6 Class locomotives, including the Mallard, the holder of the world speed record for steam locomotives, and the Flying Scotsman, notably used on the London to Edinburgh service, both of which are now in the National Railway Museum in York.

98. Oliver Cromwell. Although he ruled the country, it was as Lord Protector, not as King.

99. The 200 acres of common land in the centre of Harrogate known as The Stray was opened for public use in 1778, but a number of local families retained grazing rights, known as 'gates', which entitled them to graze either one cow, or a two-year-old horse, or four sheep. The animals legitimately placed on The Stray by the gate holders were looked after by a Stray herdsman, who could impound any animal grazing there illegally – or 'gate-crashing', as it was known.

100. Thomas Chippendale (1718-1779). The magnificent Palladian stately home of Nostell Priory near Wakefield also holds a fine collection of furniture by Chippendale, which was specially made for the house. He is believed to have also made some of the furniture in the delightful 18th-century dolls' house at Nostell Priory.

101. Harold Wilson was noted for his partiality for Gannex raincoats, which were made in the West Yorkshire mill town of Elland in the Calder Valley.

HUDDERSFIELD,
THE STATUE OF
HAROLD WILSON
2005 H151737

102. Beverley began as a religious centre that developed from the monastery founded there in the eighth century by John, Bishop of York, who was later canonised as St John of Beverley. The minster at Beverley is one of Europe's most beautiful and finest churches. The term 'Frithman' was linked with the right of sanctuary which fugitives could claim in Beverley Minster for a period of 30 days. At the end of the sanctuary period they could take the options either of going on trial for their crimes, or banishment abroad, or – unique to Beverley – of becoming a 'Frithman'. If they chose the latter, they agreed to surrender all their property to the Church, become a lifelong servant of the Church, and live in the town for the rest of their lives, albeit penniless, following their previous trades. The word 'Frith' (or 'Frid') comes from an Anglo-Saxon word for 'peace'.

BEVERLEY, MARKET PLACE 1900 45284

103. Part of Holy Trinity Church at Richmond is now used as the Regimental Museum of the Green Howards – Richmond was at the heart of the regiment's traditional recruiting area.

104. The tune of 'On Ilkla Moor Baht'at' ('On Ilkley Moor Without a Hat') is from the hymn 'Cranbrook'. It is reputed that in 1886 a church choir from Halifax was holding its summer picnic high up on the moors near Ilkley. One of the young girls, called Mary Jane, wandered off with her sweetheart. When the couple returned, the rest of the choir teased them by bursting into song with new words they had made up to the tune, including the line: 'Where's tha bin since Ah saw thee? Tha's been a-courting Mary Jane'.

105. William Wilberforce, who was born in Hull in 1759. The house where he was born, at 23-25 High Street, is now the Wilberforce House Museum, and contains an extensive collection of artefacts relating to the slave trade, the abolition of which was to take up most of his political life. William Wilberforce was elected MP for Hull at the age of 21. He was involved in many causes for reform, and in 1824 was one of the founders of the Society for the Prevention of Cruelty to Animals, now the RSPCA, but he is best remembered for his long campaign against slavery which resulted in the passing of a parliamentary bill to end the slave trade in 1807, and slavery being abolished in the British Empire in 1833 (this became law in 1834). William Wilberforce died in 1833, and was buried in Westminster Abbey. He was named the Greatest Ever Yorkshireman in a BBC poll in 2000, and in June 2005 Archbishop Desmond Tutu praised him, saying that 'Wilberforce showed that each and every one of us can make a difference'.

FRANCIS FRITH

PIONEER   VICTORIAN   PHOTOGRAPHER

Francis Frith, founder of the world-famous photographic archive, was a complex and multi-talented man. A devout Quaker and a highly successful Victorian businessman, he was philosophical by nature and pioneering in outlook. By 1855 he had already established a wholesale grocery business in Liverpool, and sold it for the astonishing sum of £200,000, which is the equivalent today of over £15,000,000. Now in his thirties, and captivated by the new science of photography, Frith set out on a series of pioneering journeys up the Nile and to the Near East.

INTRIGUE AND EXPLORATION

He was the first photographer to venture beyond the sixth cataract of the Nile. Africa was still the mysterious 'Dark Continent', and Stanley and Livingstone's historic meeting was a decade into the future. The conditions for picture taking confound belief. He laboured for hours in his wicker dark-room in the sweltering heat of the desert, while the volatile chemicals fizzed dangerously in their trays. Back in London he exhibited his photographs and was 'rapturously cheered' by members of the Royal Society. His reputation as a photographer was made overnight.

VENTURE OF A LIFE-TIME

By the 1870s the railways had threaded their way across the country, and Bank Holidays and half-day Saturdays had been made obligatory by Act of Parliament. All of a sudden the working man and his family were able to enjoy days out, take holidays, and see a little more of the world.

With typical business acumen, Francis Frith foresaw that these new tourists would enjoy having souvenirs to commemorate their days out. For the next thirty years he travelled the country by train and by pony and trap, producing fine photographs of seaside resorts and beauty spots that were keenly bought by millions of Victorians. These prints were painstakingly pasted into family albums and pored over during the dark nights of winter, rekindling precious memories of summer excursions. Frith's studio was soon supplying retail shops all over the country, and by 1890 F Frith & Co had become the greatest specialist photographic publishing company in the world, with over 2,000 sales outlets, and pioneered the picture postcard.

FRANCIS FRITH'S LEGACY

Francis Frith had died in 1898 at his villa in Cannes, his great project still growing. By 1970 the archive he created contained over a third of a million pictures showing 7,000 British towns and villages.

Frith's legacy to us today is of immense significance and value, for the magnificent archive of evocative photographs he created provides a unique record of change in the cities, towns and villages throughout Britain over a century and more. Frith and his fellow studio photographers revisited locations many times down the years to update their views, compiling for us an enthralling and colourful pageant of British life and character.

We are fortunate that Frith was dedicated to recording the minutiae of everyday life. For it is this sheer wealth of visual data, the painstaking chronicle of changes in dress, transport, street layouts, buildings, housing and landscape that captivates us so much today, offering us a powerful link with the past and with the lives of our ancestors.

Computers have now made it possible for Frith's many thousands of images to be accessed almost instantly. The archive offers every one of us an opportunity to examine the places where we and our families have lived and worked down the years. Its images, depicting our shared past, are now bringing pleasure and enlightenment to millions around the world a century and more after his death.

For further information visit: www.francisfrith.com

INTERIOR DECORATION

Frith's photographs can be seen framed and as giant wall murals in thousands of pubs, restaurants, hotels, banks, retail stores and other public buildings throughout Britain. These provide interesting and attractive décor, generating strong local interest and acting as a powerful reminder of gentler days in our increasingly busy and frenetic world.

FRITH PRODUCTS

All Frith photographs are available as prints and posters in a variety of different sizes and styles. In the UK we also offer a range of other gift and stationery products illustrated with Frith photographs, although many of these are not available for delivery outside the UK – see our web site for more information on the products available for delivery in your country.

THE INTERNET

Over 100,000 photographs of Britain can be viewed and purchased on the Frith web site. The web site also includes memories and reminiscences contributed by our customers, who have personal knowledge of localities and of the people and properties depicted in Frith photographs. If you wish to learn more about a specific town or village you may find these reminiscences fascinating to browse. Why not add your own comments if you think they would be of interest to others? See **www.francisfrith.com**

PLEASE HELP US BRING FRITH'S PHOTOGRAPHS TO LIFE

Our authors do their best to recount the history of the places they write about. They give insights into how particular towns and villages developed, they describe the architecture of streets and buildings, and they discuss the lives of famous people who lived there. But however knowledgeable our authors are, the story they tell is necessarily incomplete.

Frith's photographs are so much more than plain historical documents. They are living proofs of the flow of human life down the generations. They show real people at real moments in history; and each of those people is the son or daughter of someone, the brother or sister, aunt or uncle, grandfather or grandmother of someone else. All of them lived, worked and played in the streets depicted in Frith's photographs.

We would be grateful if you would give us your insights into the places shown in our photographs: the streets and buildings, the shops, businesses and industries. Post your memories of life in those streets on the Frith website: what it was like growing up there, who ran the local shop and what shopping was like years ago; if your workplace is shown tell us about your working day and what the building is used for now. Read other visitors' memories and reconnect with your shared local history and heritage. With your help more and more Frith photographs can be brought to life, and vital memories preserved for posterity, and for the benefit of historians in the future.

Wherever possible, we will try to include some of your comments in future editions of our books. Moreover, if you spot errors in dates, titles or other facts, please let us know, because our archive records are not always completely accurate—they rely on 140 years of human endeavour and hand-compiled records. You can email us using the contact form on the website.

Thank you!

For further information, trade, or author enquiries
please contact us at the address below:

**The Francis Frith Collection, 6 Oakley Business Park,
Wylye Road, Dinton, Wiltshire SP3 5EU England.**
Tel: +44 (0)1722 716 376 Fax: +44 (0)1722 716 881
e-mail: sales@francisfrith.co.uk **www.francisfrith.com**